Food isn't just about nour... ...enance that fuels the body and brain so it can creatively exist in the world.

Food activates a vibrant life.

Life manifests into art.

Art inspires dreams.

Logan isn't just a chef, he's an artist always dreaming of new ways to expand and enhance this weird wonderful thing we call life.

Jessica Biel

Restaurateur

THE MOST IMPORTANT THING FOR A CHEF
OR ANY ARTIST REALLY, IS TO FIND THIER OWN VOICE.
EVEN THOUGH IT USUALLY TAKES YEARS FOR ONE TO FIND IT,
LOGAN HAS BEEN LUCKY ENOUGH TO DISCOVER HIS EARLY
AND EVEN LUCKIER FOR US, HE IS ABLE TO SHARE
IT IN THIS NEW BOOK.

LIKE A COMPLETE RECIPE STRAIGHT FROM THE HEART,
LOGAN IS ABLE TO MIX PASSION INTO A DELICIOUS STORY
THAT EXCITES AND OPENS THE EYES OF THE READER
TO DISCOVER THE ENDLESS POSSIBLITIES THAT COOKING
PRESENTS.

I CAN'T WAIT TO SHARE IT WITH MY OWN
KIDS, WHO HAVE LOOKED UP TO LOGAN SINCE HE WON
THE TITLE OF MASTERCHEF JUNIOR.

GRAHAM ELLIOT

Thanks for all the Love!

Logan

PERFECT.

YOUR SKILLS HAVE IMPROVED.

RE, REALLY?

YES.

WHA, WHAT?

LOGAN, I AM PLEASED.

YOU HAVE DONE A GREAT JOB,

THANK YOU SO MUCH MASTER!

OKAY.

THIS ONE WORKS!

CHEF LOGAN, I THINK IT'S TIME FOR YOU TO FACE A BIGGER CHALLENGE.

WHAT DO YOU MEAN, MASTER?

I MEAN YOU SHOULD FOLLOW YOUR DREAMS.

THE JOURNEY STARTS WITH YOU, BUT LOGAN YOU CANNOT FINISH ALONE.

A TEAM?

ME!?

I USUALLY WORK ALONE.

SO EVERYONE CAN SEE THIS?

YES, OF COURSE.

THE FOLLOWING DAY

MAN, I DIDN'T MAKE IT.

SERIOUSLY NO ONE HAS PASSED UNTIL NOW?

YEAH.

IT MAKES ME NERVOUS.

ME TOO.

HEY, GOOD LUCK KID.

THANK YOU.

SHALL WE GET THE NEXT ONE?

IF YOU CAN COOK BETTER THAN THIS,

THEN WE WILL LET YOU USE THE BIG **KNIVES!!**

VERY WELL.

I'LL SHOW YOU

WHAT REAL COOKING IS.

WE HAVE ALL THE INGREDIENTS

THE NEXT DAY

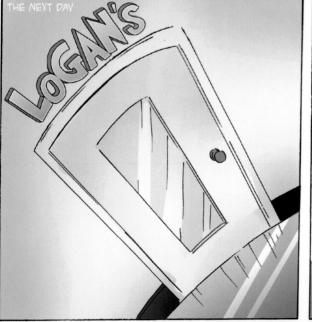

LOGAN'S

OK, WE HAVE FINISHED ENOUGH RECIPES FOR TODAY!

FINALLY!

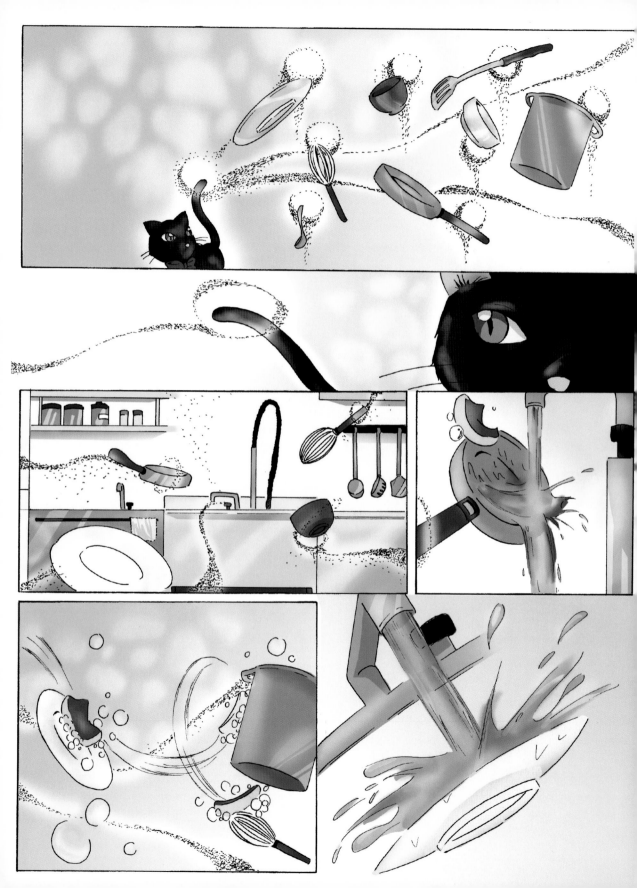

I'M SPEECHLESS.

I WISH I HAD THAT CAT.

ANYWAY, I'M KIND OF CURIOUS ABOUT THE GIRL YESTERDAY.

ME TOO! WILL SHE JOIN US?

WELL, I'M NOT SURE IF SHE WANTS TO LEAVE HER JOB. BUT SHE DIDN'T SAY NO, STILL....

WHY DON'T YOU GIVE HER ANOTHER SHOT?

YOU MEAN CALL HER AGAIN?

FRIED RICE

The first step every Chef should do is read the recipe. Reading the recipe makes sure there are no surprises.

The second step is to assemble everything you need to make the dish. Chef's call this *setting* your

Mise en Place.

Mise en Place
(meez ahn plahs)

is a French phrase for everything in place. Gather everything you need to cook the dish, from knife to potholder from onion to salt.

This will *Organize* your cooking.

Just like a Chef!

Chef Note-

Use the Mise en Place technique whenever you cook!

You will be a better *Chef* and one giant step ahead of the *competition*.

Chefs will notice!

READ IT THROUGH!

INGREDIENTS

1 TBS VEGETABLE OIL
1 TBS SESAME OIL
2 EGGS
1 GARLIC CLOVE, DICED
1/2 TSP POWDERED GINGER
1/4 CUP DICED ONION
3 CUPS COOKED COOLED RICE
1 CUP FROZEN PEAS AND CARROTS
1/2 CUP SLICED KUMQUATS
4 DROPS HOT SAUCE
4 TBS SOY SAUCE
2 GREEN ONIONS CHOPPED THIN

WOW!

STEPS

1. HEAT THE WOK OR FRYING PAN
2. ADD THE OILS AND HEAT UNTIL HOT
3. BREAK THE EGGS INTO THE PAN
4. SCRAMBLE THE EGGS
5. TOSS IN GARLIC, GINGER, & ONION
6. ADD THE RICE AND HEAT THROUGH
7. STIR IN THE PEAS AND CARROTS
8. ADD THE KUMQUATS
9. POUR IN THE SOY SAUCE & HOT SAUCE
10. PLATE
11. GARNISH WITH GREEN ONION
12. WIPE THE PLATE CLEAN!

CHEF NOTE-

STIR FRY IS A FAST WAY TO COOK.
THE PAN MUST BE HOT.
YOU HAVE TO
STIR. STIR. STIR.
CAREFULLY
BUT FAST!

Meow!

THIS IS THE MISE EN PLACE FOR THE FOOD INGREDIENTS IN THE FRIED RICE. SEE IF YOU CAN FIND THEM ALL!

COOK IT UP!

RICE

PEAS AND CARROTS

EGGS

SOY SAUCE

ONION

GREEN ONION

HOT SAUCE

GINGER

GARLIC

SESAME OIL

VEGETABLE OIL

KUMQUATS

CHEF NOTE-

I USE 2 OILS TO ADD SOME EXTRA FLAVOR. IF YOU DON'T HAVE **SESAME OIL** USE EXTRA REGULAR VEGETABLE OIL.

I USE KUMQUATS, IF YOU CAN'T FIND THEM USE SOME **ORANGE ZEST** (ABOUT 1 TBS).

ZEST IS THE GRATED OUTER SKIN OF THE ORANGE, NOT THE WHITE WHICH IS CALLED **PITH.**

ORGANIZE

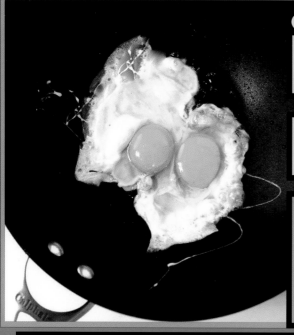

1. HEAT THE WOK OR FRYING PAN
2. ADD THE OILS AND HEAT UNTIL HOT

3. BREAK THE EGGS INTO THE PAN
4. SCRAMBLE THE EGGS.

CHEF NOTE-
TEST TO SEE IF THE OIL IS HOT BY USING THE BACK OF A WOODEN SPOON.

INSERT IT INTO THE OIL.
IF IT IS FRY HOT IT WILL BUBBLE!
REMEMBER, IT HAS TO BE WOOD!

DON'T BURN IT!

QUICKLY, SCRAMBLE THE EGGS! THEY SHOULD HAVE A BRIGHT YELLOW COLOR TO MAKE THE DISH LOOK GREAT.
MAKE THEM CHUNKY SO THEY CAN BE SEEN.

BANG!!!

NEXT...

5. TOSS IN THE GARLIC, GINGER, & ONION

CHEF NOTE-

ADD THE SPICES NOW COOK JUST A BIT AND **INFUSE** THEIR FLAVOR.

IF YOU ADD THEM EARLIER, THE **EGG** WILL ABSORB THE SPICE FLAVOR AND BE LESS **EGGY**.

EACH **INGREDIENT** NEEDS TO SHINE. Purrfect

STIR, STIR, STIR, AND FRY!

THE PAN SHOULD LOOK LIKE THIS WITH BRIGHT COLORS - DON'T BROWN!

GREAT JOB! YOU DID IT! WAY TO JOIN MY TEAM!

10. PLATE
11. GARNISH
12. WIPE THE DISH CLEAN

CHEF NOTE-

PICK A PLATE THAT SHOWS OFF YOUR FOOD.
MOST CHEFS CHOOSE **WHITE PLATES**.
I ADDED AN ADDITIONAL PLATE FOR COLOR AND STYLE.

BAAAM!

TO GARNISH THE DISH PLACE SOME OF THE **BEST** INGREDIENTS ON THE TOP TO ENTICE THE DINER.
THEN WIPE IT CLEAN.
CHEFS ALWAYS FINISH THE **DISH**.

KITCHEN EQUIPMENT AND TOOLS
CAN MAKE OR BREAK YOUR COOKING.

HERE ARE SOME OF MY FAVORITES...

TONGS PREVENT INJURIES!

TOOLS

TONGS

CHEF NOTE-
EXPERIMENT AND FIND TOOLS THAT WORK FOR YOU. WHEN YOU FIND *YOUR* FAVORITES, SAVE UP AND INVEST IN THE **BEST** QUALITY.

I CAN'T TELL YOU HOW OFTEN I USE TONGS. THEY LIFT, PLATE AND SERVE HOT FOOD. TONGS ARE LIKE HANDS THAT DON'T FEEL PAIN. I HAVE THESE COOL LOOKING ONES AND I EVEN HAVE ONE PAIR THAT BELONGED TO MY GREAT GRANDMOTHER. **TRUST ME, YOU NEED TONGS!**

MEZZALUNA

HiYA!

MEZZALUNA

CHOP

A

I LOVE IT!

THIS IS MY **FAVORITE** LITTLE CHEF TOOL.

I GOT THIS **EXACT** MEZZALUNA WHEN I WAS 4 YEARS OLD.

HOLD BOTH KNOBS AND ROCK THE BLADE. IT CHOPS AS IT **ROCKS.**

CHEF NOTE- USING THE MEZZALUNA IS EASY.

ALL **FINGERS** ARE AWAY FROM THE BLADES. IT IS A

SAFE

SAFE

SAFE

WAY TO CHOP!

A MEZZALUNA IS A DOUBLE BLADE TOOL, PERFECT FOR CHOPPING, DICING, AND MINCING! I LEARNED TO CHOP SAFELY WITH THIS TOOL. IT HAS A ROUNDED CHOPPING BOARD AND A MAT TO KEEP IT FROM MOVING.
IT IS A PERFECT TOOL FOR AN **ADVENTUROUS** LITTLE **CHEF.**

I TRY EVERYTHING!

A CHEF HAS TO BE A FOOD EXPLORER AND **ADVENTURER**.

WHEN YOU START TO CREATE YOUR OWN RECIPES AND MAKE STUNNING DISHES YOU MIGHT NEED A FLAVOR TO FINISH YOUR DISH THAT YOU JUST CAN'T FIND - THEN YOUR FLAVOR **JOURNAL** WILL REALLY COME IN HANDY!

SO BE BRAVE AND AT LEAST TASTE EVERY FOOD!
IT WILL HELP YOU BECOME A **WORLD CLASS CHEF!**

> TIME TO TALK FOOD!

I AM A FOOD EXPLORER!

CHEFS HAVE TO TRY EVERY FOOD THEY CAN FIND!

IT IS **IMPORTANT** FOR A BEGINNING CHEF TO TRY EVERYTHING!

KEEP A FLAVOR **JOURNAL**, I DO! I WRITE DOWN MY IDEAS.

CHEF GAME-

TRY THIS GAME!
GO TO THE MARKET, CHOOSE A SECTION TO **EXPLORE**.
LOOK FOR A NEW FOOD AND IF YOU CAN, BRING IT HOME AND TRY IT!
WATCH FOR SEASONAL FRESH FOODS.
RECORD YOUR EXPERIENCES IN YOUR FLAVOR JOURNAL.
JUST LIKE A **CHEF!**

KUMQUATS

KUMQUATS

ARE A CITRUS FRUIT ORIGINALLY FOUND IN ASIA. THEY GROW ON TREES WITH DARK GREEN LEAVES AND WHITE FLOWERS. THEY ARE FULL OF VITAMINS.

KUMQUATS ARE TINY BITES OF BRIGHT FLAVOR. THEY CAN BE EATEN WHOLE – PEEL, SEEDS AND ALL! USE THEM IN JAMS, DESSERTS, AND SAVORY DISHES, LIKE MY FRIED RICE.

SUBSTITUTE KUMQUATS IN A RECIPE CALLING FOR AN ORANGE AND YOU WILL BE COOKING LIKE A *CHEF.*

I HOPE YOU TRY SOME KUMQUATS SOON!

FRUIT

ORANGE

KUMQUATS

GINGER IS A **SPICE.**

SPICES, HERBS, AND AROMATICS ARE ALL PLANTS CHEFS USE. THEY HAVE STRONG FLAVORS. YOU ONLY NEED A LITTLE BIT TO ADD **FLAIR** TO YOUR FOOD.

SPICE

GINGER

GINGER COMES FROM ASIA AND INDIA. IT CAN BE FOUND AS A FRESH ROOT OR A DRY POWDER IN MOST MARKETS.
TO USE THE FRESH ROOT- SCRAPE OFF THE PEEL AND DICE OR GRATE. IT IS VERY FIBROUS SO BE CAREFUL.
GINGER HAS A STRONG SPICY FLAVOR SO YOU ONLY NEED A SMALL AMOUNT.
USE IT IN MARINADES, STIR FRY, AND EVEN PICKLED OR CANDIED.

CHEF SCIENCE

YOU CAN GROW GINGER FROM THE ROOT YOU BUY IN THE STORE, JUST PLANT IN SOIL AND WATER IT!

GINGER HAS GREAT HEALTH BENEFITS. IT HELPS YOU IF YOU HAVE A BELLY ACHE!

THE VEGETABLE BOK CHOY

Bok Choy

IS A TYPE OF ASIAN CABBAGE THAT HAS BEEN CULTIVATED IN **CHINA** FOR 5000 YEARS!

IT HAS A VERY MELLOW FLAVOR AND A GREAT **CRUNCH.** IT CAN BE EATEN RAW OR COOKED.

THERE ARE MANY DIFFERENT VARIETIES. LOOK **CLOSELY** AT THE PHOTO- THERE ARE TWO. CAN YOU SPOT THEM?

YOU CAN USUALLY FIND 2 SIZES IN THE MARKET- A LARGE FULL GROWN PLANT, ABOUT THE SIZE OF CELERY OR THE SMALL BABY **PLANTS.** THE BABY PLANTS ARE VERY TENDER. THEY ARE MY FAVORITE!

BOK CHOY
IS CALLED THE **"SOUP SPOON"** PLANT BECAUSE ITS LEAVES LOOK LIKE CHINESE SOUP SPOONS.
USE IT TO SCOOP SOME OF THE NEXT RECIPE- MAPO TOFU!
BE A FOOD **EXPLORER** TODAY!

COOKING CHALLENGE

MAPO TOFU

MAPO TOFU is a historic Chinese dish, from the Sichaun Province. It's a challenge dish because you need to be a food explorer and use your stir fry skills.

Chinese Words that define this dish are:

Ma- Numbing
La- Spicy
Tang- Hot in temperature
Xiang- Aromatic
Su- Flaky
Nen- Soft
Xian- Fresh
Huo- Live

THIS IS MY VERSION. I CHANGED IT UP, ADDED SOME EXCITING FLAVORS AND SOME VEGETABLES. IT'S FUN TO MAKE A DISH YOUR OWN!

INGREDIENTS

READY TO MAKE HISTORY? COOK UP THIS FAMOUS DISH!

LOGAN

Ingredients

2 Tbs Sesame Oil
1/2 Lb Ground Pork
2 Tbs Fermented Black Beans with Chili and Garlic
1/2-3 Tsp Chili Garlic Sauce
Optional - 1/4 Tsp Chili in Oil
1 Tsp Garlic Diced
1 Tsp Ginger Diced
1 box Firm Tofu Drained
1 1/2 Tsp Sugar
1/4 Cup Vegetable Broth
1 Tbs Corn Starch
1/2 A Lemon Juiced
(1/2 Tbs Lemon Zest)
2 Cups Bok Choy
2 Tbs Soy Sauce
2 Green Onions Sliced
1/4 Tsp Black Pepper

Wow, lots of food!

CHEF NOTE-

TOFU IS MADE OF SOY BEAN CURD. THERE ARE SEVERAL TEXTURES OF TOFU. THIS RECIPE USES FIRM.

FERMENTED BLACK BEANS ARE COMMON IN CHINESE FOOD. THEY ARE SOLD IN MOST ASIAN MARKETS.

THIS IS A SPICY DISH! ADJUST THE HEAT BY ADDING MORE OR LESS HOT CHILI PASTE AND PEPPERS.

STEPS

I HAVE NOT HEARD OF HALF THIS STUFF!

1. Heat the Wok or Pan
2. Pour in the Sesame Oil
3. Brown the Pork (alternate Mushrooms)
4. Add the Fermentated Black Beans with Chili and Garlic
5. Toss in the Chili Garlic Sauce
6. Shake in the Black Pepper, Taste, Adjust the Chilis
7. Put in the Garlic
8. Gently add the Tofu Cubes
9. Toss in the Ginger
10. Squeeze in the Juice of the Lemon
11. Mix in the Sugar and most of the Green Onion
12. Make a Slurry with the Cornstarch and Broth
13. Pour in the Slurry
14. Stir in the Bok Choy and the Soy Sauce
15. Plate
16. Garnish with Green Onions
17. Wipe the Plate

Replace the Pork with Mushrooms for a Vegan/Vegetarian dish. This dish is Gluten Free!

BOOM

Ginger

Corn Starch

Green Onion

Lemon

Broth

Bok Choy

Tofu

Pork

Garlic

Black Pepper

Chili

Chili Garlic Sauce

Sugar

Soy Sauce

Sesame Oil

Fermented Black Beans with Chili and Garlic

PREP TIME

CHEF NOTE-

THE TOFU NEEDS TO BE DRAINED AND DRIED BEFORE USE. DRAIN IT BY WRAPPING IT IN PAPER TOWELS OR A CLEAN DISH TOWEL. IT IS DELICATE, SO HANDLE IT WITH CARE. IT IS REALLY **FUN** TO CUT!

USE IT TO **PRACTICE** AND TRY TO GET PERFECT CUBES.

4. Add in the Fermented Black Beans with Chili and Garlic

5. Toss in the Chili Garlic Sauce

6 Shake in the Black Pepper. Taste, and adjust the Chilis

SPICY!

7. Put in the Garlic, Continue to Stir Fry!

THE FERMENTED BLACK BEANS DRAMATICALLY CHANGE THE COLOR AND TEXTURE OF THE DISH. THEY ADD AN EARTHY FLAVOR THAT IS FAMILAR IN CHINESE COOKING.

THE MEAT IS REALLY AROMATIC. THAT MEANS IT SMELLS DELICIOUS!

CHEF NOTE-

TOFU IS **VERY** BLAND.

IT ACTS LIKE A **SPONGE** AND ABSORBS THE FLAVORS AROUND IT.

THE AMAZING TASTES IN THE PAN WILL INFUSE INTO THE TOFU. IT WILL REALLY **POP**!

I Like Tuna!

CHEF SCIENCE- CORNSTARCH IS A UNIQUE PRODUCT. WHEN MIXED WITH LIQUID IT FORMS A NON-NEWTONIAN FLUID. THAT MEANS IT IS BOTH A LIQUID AND A SOLID AT THE SAME TIME.
EXPERIMENT-
MIX CORNSTARCH IN WATER TILL IT FORMS A THICK PASTE, HIT IT WITH YOUR HAND! IT WILL BE HARD, THEN SILDE YOUR HAND GENTLY IN AND IT WILL BE A LIQUID!! COOL, RIGHT?!

12. Make a Slurry of the Broth and Cornstarch.

13. Pour in the Slurry.

Did someone say Purry?

CHEF NOTE-

A **SLURRY** IS A RUNNY MIXTURE OF A THICKENER AND A LIQUID. MIX THE TWO TOGETHER UNTIL THERE ARE NO LUMPS. IT IS AN EASY BUT VERY IMPORTANT STEP! IF YOU CAN'T GET OUT ALL THE LUMPS DON'T PANIC, JUST USE A **STRAINER**.

CORNSTARCH IS A THICKENER FOR SAUCES. IT ONLY WORKS WHEN IT GETS HOT. THICKENED CORNSTARCH GIVES FOOD A NICE **SHINE**.

YOU CAN SEE IT IN FOOD IF YOU PAY CLOSE ATTENTION.

KA-POW!

NOW, IT REALLY NEEDS TO BE HANDLED WITH CARE. THE TOFU IS SOFT.

COOK THE BOK CHOY TILL IT IS TENDER. WE DON'T WANT IT MUSHY.

TASTE IT!

KA-POW!

Almost Done!

14. Stir in the Bok Choy and the Soy Sauce

YOU CAN STILL ADJUST THE SEASONING!

I ADD A BIT OF LEMON ZEST NOW IF THE FLAVOR IS NOT BALANCED.

CHEF NOTE-
TRADITIONAL **MAPO TOFU** HAS ONLY GREEN ONIONS. ADDING THE BOK CHOY IS MY IDEA. IF YOU ADD ANOTHER VEGETABLE LIKE BROCCOLI, THE COOKING TIME WOULD CHANGE. DON'T EVER BE AFRAID TO COOK LIKE A **CHEF** AND MAKE IT YOUR **OWN!**

IT WAS SO MUCH FUN TO BE ON A FOOD ADVENTURE. I LOVED IT! CHECK MY YOUTUBE CHANNEL TO WATCH ME COOK THIS DISH OR SHOOT ME A MESSAGE! ALL MY SOCIAL IS

LOGAN JR CHEF

I AM WORKING HARD ON THE NEXT ADVENTURE AND A NEW SET OF RECIPES!

SHAZAM! WAY TO COOK!

15. Plate
16. Garnish with a bit of Green Onion.
17. Wipe the Plate

CHEF NOTE-

WE PRACTICED AND LEARNED SOME GREAT SKILLS.

YOU'RE ON YOUR WAY TO BE A WORLD CLASS CHEF! I AM REALLY PROUD OF YOU!

Great Cooking CHEF!

THIS IS A LOGAN JR CHEF PRODUCTION

LOGAN IS A CULINARY PRODIGY WITH AWARDS INCLUDING MASTERCHEF JR WINNER SEASON 2, YOUNGEST TO COOK AT THE JAMES BEARD HOUSE, TIME MAGAZINE TOP TEEN 2016, AND MANY MORE.

"I LOVE BEING IN THE KITCHEN AND I HOPE MY BOOK HELPS YOU EXPLORE THIS AMAZING ROOM IN YOUR HOME!"

WWW.LOGANSCHEFNOTES.COM
WWW.LOGANGULEFF.COM

ISBN – 978-0-9711576-13
5/1/2017

Author Logan Guleff, Illustrator Cindy Tan, Colorist Micah Pil, Editor Chris Kautsky, Photo Editor Yen Le Nha, Tech Support Charles Morgan, Advisor K. Davidson, Photo J Burks, MOM & DAD